TV Times

Contents

PROD. NO.   TAKE   ROLL

SCENE   SOUND

DATE   CO.

Animal Actors

Written by Sharon Griggins

Rowdy walks quietly onto the set
and goes to the phone.
He picks it up and dials the numbers.
Then he barks into the phone and wags his tail.

That's today's work for Rowdy,
a big shaggy dog.

Rowdy is a TV star. Dogs, cats,
and other animals often act in TV shows.
They can make a show seem more real.
They are also very cute and funny.

Why do animals make TV shows seem more real?

What are your favorite animal films or TV programs?

Rowdy wasn't always a star.
He was a stray dog living at an animal shelter.
That's where Anne Gordon found him.
Anne had a feeling Rowdy was smart.
She took him home to join her other animals.

Anne is an animal trainer.
She trains animals to act in films and on TV.
It takes a lot of time to train an animal.
You have to do the same thing
over and over again.

Anne Gordon

Rowdy learned to hit a mark.
That means going to a spot and waiting there.
Rowdy learned to stand on a block of wood.
Anne gave him a dog treat each time he did it.
She used a smaller block of wood each day.
The block got smaller and smaller
until it was the size of a bottle top.
Now, Anne puts a tiny mark where
the director wants Rowdy to stand.

Anne Gordon

Most animal actors are dogs or cats.
But sometimes the script calls for a wild animal,
such as a deer, a raccoon, or a fox.
Anne trains them, too.

When the action begins on the set,
only the actors can talk.
Anne makes sure her animals stay quiet.
She uses hand signs to tell her animal actors
what to do.

Anne's animal actors work hard.
They train with Anne
three or four times a day.
Anne's actors love to work.
They know just what to do
when they get on a TV set.
They also know they'll always
get treats for a job well done!

When are some other times that hand signs are useful?

Stage Call

Meet Some of Anne's Animal Actors

I'm Cubby.
I can "speak," wave, crawl,
and sleep on command.
I have been on TV shows
such as *Northern Exposure*
and *Rescue 911* as well as
in lots of TV commercials.

Cubby

Willy

I'm Willy.
I can jump and
wave on command.
I was in *Little Women*,
Practical Magic,
and other films.

Mingo

I'm Mingo.
I can jump through
a hoop of fire, growl,
mark, fetch, wave, "speak,"
crawl, and play dead.
I have been in lots
of TV commercials.

I'm Casper.
I'm a raccoon.
I've been in lots
of TV commercials.

Tundra

Casper

I'm Tundra.
I'm a timber wolf.
I was in the movie
Grizzly Falls.

Is It Really Real?

Written by Terry Miller Shannon
Photographed by Mary Foley

Do you ever watch TV shows that are supposed to be real? We asked four TV-watching experts to give us their views on *Real-Life Family* and *Police Beat*. *Real-Life Family* follows the Johnson family inside their house, 24 hours a day. *Police Beat* follows police officers while they work the streets. Our question to our experts: Just how real is "reality TV"?

Give me a break! All those shows are fake.

Reality TV is totally real. Why do you think they call it "reality TV"?

I always thought reality TV showed real people and real lives. I like peeking into someone else's life. Some kids' problems seem just like mine. But other kids have problems much worse. I end up feeling sorry for them.

No way! My grandma is a police officer. She says if cops acted like they do on reality TV, the city wouldn't be safe to live in.

What's the oldest reality TV show?
Candid Camera, which began in 1948

They might be real people, but they're not acting real. Would you act naturally with cameras on you? On some shows, the cameras roll 24 hours a day. But we only get to see one hour a week.

Well, I guess TV producers could cut out whatever they want from the film. I guess they could decide what we see and what we don't see.

If the camera is on 24 hours a day, 7 days a week, that equals 168 hours. The show is one hour a week. What happens in the 167 hours we don't see?

How many people watched the last episode of Survivor's first season?

40 million

What were the five most-watched TV shows of last century?

5. *60 Minutes*
4. *Sesame Street*
3. *All in the Family*
2. *I Love Lucy*
1. *M*A*S*H*

I guess they've got to do something to make it exciting! If the show's dead boring, people won't watch and the network will cancel it.

I suppose that means they could take a silly fight and turn it into a big deal. If I fight with my sister, it doesn't last long. But if we were on TV, it could seem like we were going to fight forever.

I think these shows should be called "not-reality TV." I mean your average, everyday person hardly wants to be filmed 24 hours a day. How are people chosen for reality TV?

Maybe the money makes it all worth it. I'm pretty sure they get paid.

I don't think they get paid! I don't think they're told what to say. But maybe they are.

How would we know? Maybe we could write to the producers and find out just how real reality TV is.

How much money do MTV's Real World housemates get?
Zero. Zilch. Not one thing.

How many people auditioned for MTV's Real World?
More than 35,000.

WILD TV

Written by Sharon Griggins

How do you get a great white shark on TV?
Just dress up your camera like its favorite meal!

Photographing wildlife is an exciting job.
But it's dangerous, too.
You can't just swim up to a shark and say, "Smile!"
Getting the shots we see on nature shows
takes brains, practice, and a bit of luck.
The secret is to get close to the animal.
That can be hard because most animals
go away when they see humans coming.
Other animals might charge or attack.
Good wildlife photographers know
just how close to get.

TV camera people are called photographers or videographers. This videographer is filming from inside a shark cage.

17

You have to think like the animal you plan to film.
You have to know its habits.
Where does it live? What does it eat? Where does it go for water?
Most wildlife photographers study nature and animals.
They know the right time and place to get the best pictures.

When an animal gets used to seeing a human with a camera, it lets the photographer get closer. This young leopard is being filmed in Indonesia.

How would you feel if you were this close to a wild animal?
How do you think the videographer felt?

A Bactrian camel and her calf are filmed in the Gobi desert.

One trick for getting close to wild animals is to build a small hut called a "blind." The photographer hides in the blind.
The outside of the blind seems to blend into the ground or trees around it.

A bird comes back to its chicks while a camera crew watches from its blind.

A videographer films macaque monkeys in Japan.

What sort of person do you think would make a good wildlife photographer?

Getting the perfect shot of an animal
may take weeks.
You have to be in the right place at the right time.
Your camera has to be ready.
You might have to wait in the rain, wind, or snow.

Wildlife photographers do their work
because they love nature.
It is important work.
The more we see and understand wild animals,
the more we will care about their future.

A sound technician records
a black-tailed prairie dog.

21

How I Learned to Videotape Animals

I saw a nature show on TV.
I wanted to make a TV show
about wild animals, too!
My dad said I could use our video camera.
I started at home by filming my dog.
Then, we went to the park
to film birds and squirrels.

Later, we went to the zoo
to videotape all sorts of animals.
I was very still and quiet.
I filmed for a long time.
I filmed the lions at feeding time.

Dad and I watched
my nature show on our TV.

AAARGH!

Mackie Jackson, I'm 12¾ and it's ALL OVER.

Crazy Bunny. Yeah!

Crazy Bunny says eat a carrot a day.

October 2

My life is over.

My mom signed me up to try out

for a TV commercial.

But it's for No-Sweat DEODORANT!

What was she thinking?

Couldn't she find something REALLY embarrassing?

Discuss my pits in front of millions?

NEVER!!

October 3

WAYS TO AVOID BEING IN A COMMERCIAL

• Pretend to be sick

• Talk funny

• Paste wigs in armpits

• Pierce nose

Welcome to
Mackie's House o' Fun
(NOT)

Wigs

Nose ring

(You don't even want to go there!)

October 3, later

Mom will be there.

My plans won't work.

October 3, later still

Save me!

Got that sinking feeling!

Mackie looking as cool as ever...

October 4

Now I NEED No-Sweat.

October 5

The tryout is tomorrow! Help!

October 6

This office is slicker than a spaceship.

The TV people stare at us.

They let some (lucky) kids leave.

Next, we each have to say our names and hobbies.

"I'm Mackie. I enjoy not being in dumb commercials."

(Not really.)

They send more kids home.

Only a million kids are left.

Nobody's talking.

I'm not nervous.

No, really, not at all.

I mean it.

My brilliant career.

October 6, later

I've learned the lines, but I don't want them to pick me.

Honestly.

Uh-oh. They're calling kids in, two by two.

I can't swallow.

My spit has disappeared.

Crazy Bunny to the rescue...

Mom (not a happy camper)

My brilliant plan

Feel as small as a bug.

Scuttle away and find a rock to crawl under...

October 6, later

"Rafiq Ghurabi... Mackie Jackson!"

Mom whispers good luck.

Right. If I had ANY luck, I'd be somewhere else.

Like, under a rock.

I follow a little guy carrying a huge backpack.

I look back toward the exit and freedom.

Mom waves.

There is no escape.

Sigh!

Peace

Shopping for Mom's birthday present

Rafiq!

Worm (me)

I peek in the door.

The TV people are sitting around a table.

They look bored.

My torturers, the TV guys

Old school hairdo

Try-hard shades

Back combing (so last century)

What can I say?

Tragic disco shirt

29

Rafiq opens his backpack.

Is he going to e-mail for help?

He pulls out pretend tattoos, fake glasses,

and green hair goop.

He says, "This should do the trick!"

We start to laugh and then go to work.

A big thumbs-up from Crazy Bunny!

←—The olds having a fit!

Superstars in the making!

Rafiq

Excellent!

Mackie

We go in. The TV people whisper together.

They smile like "Are they JOKING?"

But, as Rafiq and I say our lines,

something funny happens.

We aren't bad!

Mom

October 9

No way. The No-Sweat people want us!

Rafiq is thrilled.

He says he'd hoped our tricks

would make us stand out...

and get us the job!

"WHAT?!?" I scream.

But...

Hmm.

Rafiq can make anything fun.

The TV people were good sports.

Mom's dancing with joy.

Hey, I think I'm going to be a star!

Fame

Darlings!

Adoring masses!

We love you Mackie!

Mackie to the max!

Celebrity-type sneakers

31

Index